MORE®

My Ongoing Recovery Experience

The Basics

Workbook 1

This workbook belongs to _____

Hazelden
Publishing

Hazelden Publishing
Center City, Minnesota 55012
hazelden.org/bookstore

ISBN: 978-1-61649-808-5

Editor's note

The names, details, and circumstances may have been changed to protect the privacy of those mentioned in this publication.

This publication is not intended as a substitute for the advice of health care professionals.

Readers should be aware that websites listed in this work may have changed or disappeared between when this work was written and when it is read.

The Twelve Steps are reprinted from *Alcoholics Anonymous,* 4th ed. (New York: Alcoholics Anonymous World Services, 2001), 59–60.

Alcoholics Anonymous, AA, and the Big Book are registered trademarks of Alcoholics Anonymous World Services, Inc.

The content in this workbook is from the Hazelden Betty Ford Foundation's My Ongoing Recovery Experience (MORE®) online aftercare program.

Cover design: Theresa Jaeger Gedig
Interior design: Terri Kinne
Developmental editor: Jodie Carter
Production editor: April Ebb
Copyeditor: Victoria Tirrel

Contents

Duplicating this page is illegal. Do not copy this material without written permission from the publisher.

iii

Overview of the MORE Program

MORE (My Ongoing Recovery Experience) is a program that offers education and guidance on essential recovery topics that will help you successfully manage the critical first year of your recovery. MORE can also be used for those just starting treatment or for those who have been in recovery for a while and want to renew or deepen their knowledge and skills.

Most addiction relapses—taking a drink or using after a period of abstinence—occur within the first eighteen months of recovery, with the majority happening in the first six months after an individual leaves treatment. It is important to identify your high-risk situations that pose a threat to your recovery and to make a plan for them, which will help you avoid relapse. Research suggests that if you can remain abstinent for at least one year after treatment, you have a good chance of staying sober—and maintaining your recovery for the rest of your life.

Overview of This Workbook: *The Basics*

Workbook 1 will help you build a stable lifestyle that supports your sobriety by making your living environment safe and creating healthy daily routines.

What Key Topics Are Covered?

In this workbook, you will learn how to create a safe living environment and how to build a daily schedule that supports your recovery. You will discover that there are some medications that people in recovery should avoid and learn about safe alternatives. You will learn about the Twelve Steps, the importance of going to meetings, how to find a sponsor, and how a sponsor can help with recovery. You will explore powerlessness as the foundation of Step One, learn about relapse basics and the warning signs of relapse, create a relapse prevention plan, and learn how to deal with a relapse if it does happen. You will receive guidance on how to talk about your recovery with friends, family, and coworkers.

This workbook includes a variety of resources, such as:

- a Thought for the Day meditation or quote to accompany each topic
- education and skill-building on important early recovery topics
- activities that will help you practice self-reflection and put what you are learning into action
- "pocket power" Recovery Resources that you can keep with you for quick reference
- suggestions for Big Book readings on important topics
- websites for other recovery resources

As you complete the lessons in this workbook, you should start to see real growth and transformation in your life as you continue deeper work in recovery principles.

Create a Safe Living Environment

Thought for the Day	*"A little knowledge that acts is worth infinitely more than much knowledge that is idle."*
	— KAHLIL GIBRAN

LIVING SAFELY

Your first responsibility is to live safely. This means clearing your environment of alcohol and other drugs, and anything that went with them. We call this process "trashing your stash." There is no room for alcohol or other drugs in your life because there is no such thing as controlled use of alcohol or other drugs for those of us who have the disease of addiction.

We must practice complete abstinence. For us, "one drink is too many, and a thousand are never enough." Abstinence is the first step toward lifelong recovery. By remaining free of substances, you can stop the vicious cycle of negative consequences. Clearing your environment of anything that reminds you of drug use is the first step in protecting your abstinence.

ACTIVITY

TRASH YOUR STASH

This activity will help you learn how to make your living environment safe. Replace your stash with things that will help your recovery, such as Twelve Step books, the Serenity Prayer, or your favorite recovery slogans. Don't do this alone! Ask your sponsor or a friend in recovery to go through your home and car with you to make sure you completely trash your stash—including things such as smoking pipes, bongs, or needles. Make sure you get rid of anything that will trigger memories of drinking and using.

Duplicating this page is illegal. Do not copy this material without written permission from the publisher.   3

When you go home to trash your stash, you can use the Trash Your Stash Checklist to help you remove anything that reminds you of using. There is an extra copy of this checklist in the Recovery Resources section at the end of this workbook.

TRASH YOUR STASH CHECKLIST

ADD TO YOUR ENVIRONMENT	REMOVE FROM YOUR ENVIRONMENT
☐ Place Twelve Step literature, the Serenity Prayer, favorite recovery slogans, and the Big Book in the places you used to have your stash.	☐ Remove all alcohol, other drugs, and paraphernalia from your environment.
☐ Add contact information for your sponsor, your counselor, and friends from Twelve Step meetings to your cell phone.	☐ Delete your drug dealers' and/or drinking buddies' phone numbers from your address book. Remove any notes or pieces of paper with names and numbers of dealers and/or drinking buddies.
☐ Bookmark positive websites on your computer (such as Alcoholics Anonymous and Narcotics Anonymous).	☐ Remove the email addresses of drug dealers and/or drinking buddies.
☐ Save music and movies that will provide uplifting messages to support your sobriety.	☐ Remove bookmarks from websites that trigger your desire to drink or use drugs.
☐ Use medications that have been prescribed to you only as directed. Mark medications on your calendar or smartphone to remind you to take them on time.	☐ Get rid of music, concert T-shirts, hats, and other things that trigger your desire to drink or use drugs.
☐ Attach a schedule of local Twelve Step meetings to your refrigerator.	☐ Get rid of movies with drinking or drug themes.
	☐ Get rid of any addictive medications.

Who will help you trash your stash? *Fill in name(s) below.*

_____

_____

Are you fully committed to trashing your stash? How will you feel after trashing your stash?

_____

_____

■

What Are Twelve Step Groups Such as Alcoholics Anonymous?

Alcoholics Anonymous (AA) is a group of people who help each other recover from alcoholism. Members attend local AA group meetings and do not pay fees. The Twelve Steps of AA are principles that present a way of living used by members of AA to keep the disease of addiction at bay. There are similar Twelve Step groups, such as Narcotics Anonymous (NA), a group that helps people abstain from using other drugs. Al-Anon is a Twelve Step fellowship that offers hope and help to families and friends affected by someone else's drug use. Alateen is a group for teenagers affected by a parent's or someone else's alcoholism or other addiction. Find meetings by visiting aa.org, na.org, or al-anon.org.

What Is the Big Book?

The Big Book is a nickname for the core text of the AA organization. The Big Book contains personal stories from recovering alcoholics of inspiration, experience, strength, and hope. You can use the Big Book to help you work the Twelve Steps of AA or to look up topics such as spirituality, forgiveness, or making amends. Reading it will help you stay focused on your recovery.

ACTIVITY

ASK FOR A SUPPORTIVE LIVING ENVIRONMENT

Besides trashing your stash, you may also have to deal with living with others who use. Of course, it's best to live in an environment with people who *never* drink or use drugs of any kind, but if you can't totally control your living environment, this activity provides some tips for coping.

If you live with people who use and they *don't* have an addiction, there are things you can do to help them support you. Check the items below you are willing to do:

☐ Ask them not to use at home. Many won't mind. It's not that important to them.

☐ Have an honest discussion about your addiction and the fact that living around people who use alcohol or other drugs is difficult for you.

☐ Encourage them to attend an open Twelve Step meeting and Al-Anon or another Twelve Step program for family members or friends.

continued

- Provide literature and other resources so they better understand the disease of addiction. Also, give them their own copy of the Big Book.

- Plan fun, nondrinking activities together, and don't attend events together where there may be drinking.

- Ask them to seek counseling with you, or go by yourself.

If you live with someone who uses and he or she *does* have an addiction or refuses to stop, there are still things you can do. You can:

- Realize that your sobriety may make this person feel uncomfortable or angry. Be prepared for this to happen, and don't let it affect your motivation to stay abstinent.

- Attend a lot of meetings, talk with your sponsor, and be prepared to talk with others in your support network to help you deal with this stress.

- Keep focused on your first priority—your own sobriety. Do what it takes to remain sober.

- Get help from others to try to get this person to pursue treatment.

- Consider a different living situation, such as sober housing, at least in the short term.

Being around people who use alcohol or other drugs is especially dangerous in early recovery. Seeing people drinking or using drugs is a trigger that will cause you to think about and have cravings for drugs. And this could lead you to relapse.

Relapse Trigger Process

Trigger Thought Craving Use

It's important to remember that you must practice complete abstinence because you are powerless to control your use of alcohol and other drugs. Don't fool yourself into thinking you can drink like your nonaddicted friends or family members.

Write down any concerns you have about asking supportive family and friends for assistance in creating a healthy living environment.

_____

_____

_____

_____

_____

_____

EVALUATE YOUR MEDICATIONS

As part of creating a safe living space, you also need to evaluate prescription (Rx) and over-the-counter (OTC) medications that exist in your home. Many medications, both OTC and Rx, have mood-altering effects, and people in recovery should avoid them. Not only do these medications have addiction potential of their own, but they could also cause you to relapse.

General Guidelines
Be upfront with your health care providers, such as your physician and dentist, about your addiction. If they are aware of your addiction, they can prescribe or recommend more suitable medications.

Read all labels. This cannot be stressed enough. Many OTC medications contain one or more ingredients that you should not be taking. Make sure you check both the active and inactive ingredients because many contain alcohol as an "inactive" ingredient. If a medication that you should not be taking is deemed medically necessary by your health care professional, make sure you notify your sponsor as well as your recovery team (counselor or peer coach). It is also important that you have a plan for use as well as a plan to stop use.

Medications Safe for Use by People in Recovery
The Medication Guide for People in Recovery is found in the Recovery Resources section at the end of this workbook. This offers guidance on medications that are safe for use by people in recovery. Use the medication guide as a reference

Duplicating this page is illegal. Do not copy this material without written permission from the publisher.

7

you can take with you to the doctor or pharmacy. Because there are so many medications available, it is impossible to list all the medications that you should not use. This list references common reasons why some medications are safe to use while others are not recommended for people in recovery. It also lists examples of medications that are safe and those that you should avoid.

The medication guide is not meant to replace the advice of your physician, pharmacist, or other health care professional. If you have questions about a specific medication not listed in this guide, contact your physician, pharmacist, or counselor.

Write down any concerns you have about evaluating your medications or talking with your physician about medications.

_____

_____

_____

_____

_____

_____

SUMMARY OF ACTIVITIES

This lesson focused on creating a safe living environment. Make sure you use the Trash Your Stash Checklist to help you remove anything that reminds you of using. Ask supportive family and friends for assistance in creating a healthy living environment for your recovery. Use the Medication Guide for People in Recovery (in the Recovery Resources section at the end of this workbook) to thoroughly evaluate your medications, and use it as a reference you can take with you to the doctor or pharmacy.

Build a Healthy Daily Schedule

Thought for the Day	*Planning my day is one big step I can take to remove the opportunity to drink alcohol or use other drugs.*

It's pretty safe to say that no schedule and no routines = no sobriety. One of your early recovery goals is to remove the opportunity to drink alcohol or use other drugs.

Getting rid of your stash was a start. The next task is to plan your day—hour by hour. It may sound crazy, but this simple task has helped thousands in the early weeks of recovery.

Before planning a healthy daily schedule that will support your recovery, think about the routines you had when you were using. Did you use when you were home alone? With friends? After payday? When you were stressed at work or school?

ACTIVITY

IDENTIFY HIGH-RISK SITUATIONS

In the past, there were probably certain days or times that you would go to a bar or to social events where people might be drinking or using other drugs. These are high-risk situations. A high-risk situation includes people, places, or situations that can expose you to thoughts of using drugs or that create high stress for you.

Answer the following questions to identify your high-risk situations and learn about strategies that will help you replace these with healthy activities.

1. Are there certain times of day that are very stressful for you? Are there days or times (such as payday or the weekend) when you previously used drugs? Describe some of your old routines and how they put you at risk for relapse.

continued

Duplicating this page is illegal. Do not copy this material without written permission from the publisher.

9

_____

_____

_____

_____

_____

_____

_____

_____

➡ **STRATEGIES:**

- Plan to call your sponsor or a friend in recovery at this time.

- Plan a fun sober activity to do during this time.

- If possible, attend a Twelve Step meeting during this period of time.

- Plan to be with other people who are supportive of your recovery during this time.

- Plan to work on your program during this time—read the Big Book, Twelve Step literature, or a meditation book; spend time in meditation.

2. Are there stretches of time when you will be alone?

_____

_____

_____

_____

_____

_____

_____

_____

➡ **STRATEGIES:**

- Try to limit the long periods of time that you are spending alone.

- Plan to call your sponsor or a friend in recovery at this time.

- Plan a fun sober activity to do during this time.

- If possible, attend a Twelve Step meeting during this time.

- Plan to be with other people who are supportive of your recovery during this time.

3. Are there events that will be stressful for you?

_____

_____

_____

_____

_____

_____

_____

➡ **STRATEGIES:**

- If possible, avoid this stressful situation.

- Limit the number of stressful situations you have in your day. Can you say no to something?

- Before you go to this stressful event, call your sponsor or a friend in recovery. Talk through strategies to handle the stress.

- Have a plan of "escape" if the situation becomes too stressful—drive separately to the event, for example.

- Make a plan to call your sponsor or a friend in recovery right after the stressful event.

- Go to a Twelve Step meeting right after the stressful event.

- Plan an enjoyable sober activity to do right after the stressful event.

- Spend some time in meditation before and after the event.

- Use breathing exercises to calm yourself during the event.

continued

4. Are there any high-risk situations for you this week? Avoid high-risk situations—places where you used to use and places where other people will be using.

Are there places you should avoid?

_____

_____

_____

_____

Are there people you should avoid?

_____

_____

_____

_____

➡ Tips for avoiding places:

• Take a different route so you avoid certain places.

• Ask people to meet you at locations that will not trigger use for you—for example, meet at a coffee shop rather than a bar.

• Ask other people to drive, so you aren't tempted to go places you shouldn't.

• Turn down invitations to events where alcohol or other drugs might be present.

➡ Tips for avoiding people:

• Politely say no to people you need to avoid.

• Honestly tell people that you are in recovery now and need to protect your sobriety.

• Get rid of the phone numbers and email addresses of people you used to use with.

• Don't go to places where you know these people will be.

• Avoid all contact, even by phone, with these people.

If you can't avoid a situation, use these coping strategies:

- Ask someone who is supportive of your recovery to go with you.

- Talk through the situation with your sponsor or a friend in recovery before going.

- Write out a plan of how you are going to handle the situation. Create this plan with the help of a friend in recovery. Carry this plan with you.

- Commit to call your sponsor or a friend in recovery right after the event or situation.

- Have an "escape" plan to get out of the situation if it becomes too difficult for you.

- Plan to go to a Twelve Step meeting right afterward.

ACTIVITY

CREATE A DAILY SCHEDULE

Now that you know your high-risk situations and strategies to avoid them, you will need to create a new daily schedule that replaces your high-risk routines with healthy activities. Healthy routines include attending Twelve Step meetings, such as Alcoholics Anonymous (AA) or Narcotics Anonymous (NA). Exercising or going for coffee with sober friends can be helpful new routines that can help you minimize thoughts or reminders of using drugs. Your goal is to keep your day filled with positive activities.

Once you've reviewed your old schedule and thought of ways to improve it, you're ready to create a new, healthy daily schedule. When you've completed your schedule, it will look similar to the example on the next page. Make sure you don't have long periods of time when you are alone. Make sure you add notes to help you remember specific things you need to avoid.

Make multiple copies of the blank Daily Schedule form (found in the Recovery Resources section at the end of this workbook) to plan each day of your week. A sample schedule is shown on the next page.

Make sure you plan a healthy activity for every hour of the day, every day of the week.

Example of Daily Schedule

Daily Schedule

Day of the Week (circle one): T   W   Th   F   Sat   Sun

A.M.	6:00:	Sleep
	7:00:	Wake up
	8:00:	Sober Friends meeting
	9:00:	Work
	10:00:	Work
	11:00:	Work
P.M.	Noon:	Work
	1:00:	Work
	2:00:	Work
	3:00:	Work
	4:00:	Work
	5:00:	Gym
	6:00:	Dinner and TV with family
	7:00:	Call my sponsor
	8:00:	Read meditation book
	9:00:	Shower and get clothes ready for next day's work
	10:00:	Go to bed
	11:00:	Sleep

Notes:

Be sure to have dinner with sober friends. Don't go to dinner at any restaurants that have a bar.

Be sure to go to bed on time and not stay up too late. I need a minimum of 8 hours of sleep every day.

Reminders

Ask yourself these questions:

- Have I filled in gaps of time?
- Have I scheduled time to connect with my sponsor and Higher Power?
- Have I identified and planned for high-risk situations?
- Did I make my recovery activities a priority?
- Is my day too busy or too stressful?
- Did I schedule time to attend at least one Twelve Step meeting per week?
- Have I shared my plan with others?

Plan your week, but live in recovery one day at a time.
Keep your focus on doing your best today.

Tips for Creating Your Daily Schedule

As you create your daily schedule, review it and ask the following:

☐ Have I scheduled regular times for going to bed and waking up?

☐ Are there any risky situations in my schedule? (If yes, replace these with healthy alternatives.)

☐ Did I schedule time to call my sponsor and attend at least one meeting per week?

☐ Did I schedule healthy activities to cover the times when my cravings are the strongest?

☐ Is my day too busy or too stressful?

☐ Are there gaps of time where I have no plans? (If so, plan to call a supportive friend.)

☐ Did I schedule times to take prescribed medications for any health issues I have?

Make Time for Sober Fun

In early recovery, you may feel as if you don't know how to "have fun" without using alcohol or other drugs. Maybe things other people think are fun—like going to the movies or playing games—are really boring compared to the fun you had with your friends who used drugs. This is a common feeling that will change after you spend more time in recovery. As your brain and body heal, you will start to enjoy simple things you can do for fun.

Make time for healthy, sober fun in your schedule.

Are you interested in any of the following activities?

☐ Try a new sport.

☐ Take a class.

☐ Play board games with friends.

☐ Go to the zoo.

☐ Finish a project you abandoned long ago.

☐ Learn a craft.

☐ Go for a hike or walk.

☐ Watch a funny movie or TV show and laugh without the aid of mood-altering substances.

continued

After you've determined which activities you are interested in doing, make adjustments to your schedule if needed.

Keep this schedule with you at all times. If you use a smartphone or computer, make sure you add your schedule to your calendar so you see it every day.

Sticking to the healthy daily schedule each hour may seem extreme, but it will help you more than you can imagine. With practice, those healthy plans will become a natural part of your daily routine.

If you absolutely can't avoid a stressful activity, make sure your sponsor or counselor knows and can support you.

BALANCE WORK OR SCHOOL WITH RECOVERY

If you are working or are a volunteer or student, remember to practice these tips to help you balance those duties with your recovery:

- **Prioritize your activities.** The key to scheduling is having the right priorities. This means making time for recovery-related activities, such as attending Twelve Step meetings, talking to your sponsor, and working the Steps.

- **Make time for short breaks.** When you can, try to take a break from work to stretch, walk around, get a drink of water, or say "hello" to a coworker or friend.

- **Take one thing at a time.** When deadlines and other demands start to overwhelm you, break down the work into smaller tasks. Pick one urgent task and work on it, then move on to the next one.

Do you have any concerns about managing work or school obligations while still making your recovery a top priority? Describe these concerns below or share them with your group.

_____

_____

_____

_____

_____

_____

_____

_____

_____

_____

ACTIVITY

RECOVERY WALLET CARD

This activity will ask you to start to complete a Recovery Wallet Card that will include a list of your supporters, your reasons for recovery, Twelve Step meetings near you, and tips for ending a relapse

It will be easier for you to stick to a healthy daily schedule if you (1) know whom you can call for support, (2) stay focused on the important reasons why you are working on recovery, and (3) know when and where you can attend a nearby meeting.

After you fill out the information in the Recovery Wallet Card, it will look similar to the card shown on the next page.

continued

You build your future with your daily habits.

Recovery Wallet Card Example

My supporters:	**My reasons for being in recovery:**
Name: Wesley A.	1. Become someone whom I and others respect.
Phone: 612-495-XXXX	2. Heal with my mom/love my mom.
Name: Jennifer A.	3. Be good to myself and others. Happy life.
Phone: 651-375-XXXX	
Name: Mike R. (my sponsor)	
Phone: 651-984-XXXX	*"One day at a time"*

My recovery resources/meetings:	**END YOUR LAPSE**
Name: Sober Friends (Cafe Coffee Shop) **Address:** 9459 W. 28th St., Minneapolis, MN 55408 **Day/Time:** M–F, 7 a.m.	1. ASK FOR HELP TO STOP USING 2. GET OUT OF THE SITUATION 3. REPEAT THE FOLLOWING
Name: Big Book Study Group **Address:** 4241 Lyndale Ave., Minneapolis, MN 55408 **Day/Time:** Wed., 6 p.m.	• *I made a mistake.* • *I feel guilty, but that's normal.* • *I will stay calm.*
Name: Solution Seekers (Santi Community Center) **Address:** 1945 Hawkens St. NW, Eagan, MN 55122 **Day/Time:** Sat., 6 p.m.	• *One slip does not equal failure.* • *I can learn from this experience.* • *I can recommit to my recovery.*

A blank Recovery Wallet Card for you to fill out is found in the Recovery Resources section at the end of this workbook.

SUMMARY OF ACTIVITIES

This lesson focused on helping you create healthy routines. Make sure you complete the Daily Schedule form and keep it with you to help you follow your schedule. Keep in mind that, over time, your living situation will change, and you will need to keep updating your schedule so that it reflects your current work, school, or other responsibilities, while still making time for your positive recovery activities, such as Twelve Step meetings, time with sober friends, and spiritual activities. Make sure to also keep your Recovery Wallet Card with you at all times as a reminder of the people you can count on for support and where to go to meetings. Use the Recovery Wallet Card to also reflect on your reasons for being in recovery, which can help you remember why you are doing this important work.

Learn about the Twelve Steps

Thought for the Day	*"Rarely have we seen a person fail who has thoroughly followed our path."*
	— ALCOHOLICS ANONYMOUS

THE TWELVE STEPS

Until 1935, there was no known addiction treatment that worked. Later that year, Bill W. and Dr. Bob started a group called Alcoholics Anonymous (AA) and eventually wrote the Twelve Steps to offer simple, straightforward principles, or basic truths, that people can follow to recover from addiction.

The Twelve Steps express the fundamental principles used by members of AA to transform their lives from moral decay to the spiritual fitness needed to keep the disease of addiction (also known as a "substance use disorder") at bay. As people with addiction, we didn't know how to live sober. We bounced through life, going from one high to another, acting as if we were in control. The Twelve Steps offer us a basic guide on how to approach lifelong recovery.

Twelve Step Groups

There are many Twelve Step groups based on the set of guiding principles that were originally developed by AA. This includes Narcotics Anonymous (NA) and many others.

ALCOHOLICS ANONYMOUS (AA)

AA members share a common goal—to help each other stay sober. At meetings, members explore the principles behind the Twelve Steps. They tell their stories, answer questions from newcomers, and help each other stay sober just for today. They listen, and they keep what they hear private. By tradition, AA groups are

Duplicating this page is illegal. Do not copy this material without written permission from the publisher.

19

run by members; no one person or group of people is in charge. Membership is free (supported through member contributions). AA is not religious or denominational. Members are encouraged to define their own version of a Higher Power. Visit aa.org to find a meeting near your zip code. Visit aa-intergroup.org to find online meetings that are available where you can use online chat or join an audio/video meeting. Both require an internet connection.

NARCOTICS ANONYMOUS (NA)

NA is based on the Twelve Steps of AA and offers similar peer support meetings. NA helps people recover from using drugs such as heroin, prescription painkillers, and other narcotic drugs. Membership is free and requires nothing except the desire to stop using drugs and the willingness to show up for meetings. Visit na.org to find meetings near your zip code.

WORKING THE STEPS

The Twelve Steps offer us a spiritual process to help us transform our lives from unmanageability into physical and spiritual health. The process in the Steps follows a logical sequence, starting with Step One and going through Step Twelve. You should begin by working the Steps in this order, and be careful not to cut corners or skip over any Steps. You can find a list of the Twelve Steps in the Recovery Resources section at the end of this workbook.

These basic principles of the Twelve Steps ask us to *accept* that we have the disease of addiction, *surrender* our ego, improve our way of living by paying attention to how we live each day, improve our thoughts and behaviors, and promptly admit our wrongs and then make amends if needed. We practice *serenity* by accepting ourselves, others, and things that are outside of our control and by turning these over to the wisdom of a *Higher Power*. The Steps also ask us to pay it forward by *helping others*.

Small steps forward are still steps.

IDENTIFY THE PRINCIPLES THAT ARE IMPORTANT TO YOU

Check the boxes below to identify areas of your life that you would like to improve by working the Steps. As you learn more about the Twelve Steps, you will see them as a process that will help you get there.

- ☐ accepting that you have the disease of addiction
- ☐ surrendering your ego
- ☐ improving your thoughts and behaviors
- ☐ promptly admitting your wrongs
- ☐ making amends, where needed
- ☐ practicing serenity
- ☐ leaning on the wisdom of a Higher Power
- ☐ helping others

THE THREE PHASES OF WORKING THE STEPS

The Steps can be divided into three phases that show how you will grow as you work them.

The Three Phases

Preparation	Transformation	Continued Transformation
Steps One through Three	**Steps Four through Nine**	**Steps Ten through Twelve**
The first three Steps prepare you for change. They focus on understanding your disease and knowing and seeking the solution.	Once you know the problem and the solution, you need to take action. By following these six Steps (also called "Action Steps" in AA), you will begin to see your life transformed.	Recovery is a lifelong journey. These three Steps (also called "Maintenance Steps" in AA) focus on actions you can take to continue your growth and maintain the success you have achieved day by day, for a lifetime.

Keep in mind that we don't just work the Steps once and then never return to them. Recovery is about continuously working the Steps as part of our healthy lifestyle. Each time you work a Step, you will gain more from it because you are still growing as a person.

EMBRACE THE GIFTS OF THE TWELVE PROMISES

The Big Book (pages 83–84) outlines the twelve promises of sober living. These twelve promises explain the gifts we receive by working the Steps. Some gifts happen quickly, and others may take time. Be patient and ask others about the work they did to get there.

As you read the promises below, circle those gifts you are most excited to receive, and then write down why these are especially important to you.

The twelve promises say:

1. If we are painstaking about this phase of our development, we will be amazed before we are half way through.

2. We are going to know a new freedom and a new happiness.

3. We will not regret the past nor wish to shut the door on it.

4. We will comprehend the word serenity and we will know peace.

5. No matter how far down the scale we have gone, we will see how our experience can benefit others.

6. That feeling of uselessness and self-pity will disappear.

7. We will lose interest in selfish things and gain interest in our fellows.

8. Self-seeking will slip away.

9. Our whole attitude and outlook upon life will change.

10. Fear of people and of economic insecurity will leave us.

11. We will intuitively know how to handle situations which used to baffle us.

12. We will suddenly realize that God is doing for us what we could not do for ourselves.

These gifts are important to me because

_____

_____

_____

_____

UNDERSTAND THE SPIRITUAL COMPONENT
OF THE TWELVE STEPS

All Twelve Step programs promote spirituality, rather than promoting specific beliefs about religion or God. The Steps teach us that addiction is the by-product of a spiritual problem that requires a spiritual solution. A belief in God or religion is not necessary. What is necessary is grasping the truth that our own human power (self-will) has proven ineffective against the disease of addiction. This means you need the help of others; you don't have all the answers.

Step One:
"We admitted we were powerless over alcohol [or other drugs]—
that our lives had become unmanageable."

In Step One, we accept powerlessness by admitting that we have a problem. We realize that, alone, we are powerless over the mind- and mood-altering substances we trusted with our life. We learn that we are not bad people and that we don't have to be alone anymore.

Step Two:
"Came to believe that a Power greater than ourselves
could restore us to sanity."

In Step Two, we believe a "Power greater than ourselves" can restore us to sanity. This means we admit that we need help. We begin to understand addiction as a spiritual problem that requires a spiritual solution. We accept that we need to find a loving, guiding power we can really trust to help us. This guiding force is our Higher Power.

You don't have to identify your Higher Power right now—
you just need to know that you aren't it.

FINDING YOUR HIGHER POWER

Your idea of a Higher Power that you can trust will be uniquely your own. Some people may call their Higher Power "God." For others, it is the wisdom or energy of nature and the universe. Some people in early recovery find it helpful to think of "God" as their Twelve Step "Group of Drunks" or the "Good Orderly Direction" they are now seeking. Some consider their Higher Power to be a group of recovery friends whose collective wisdom is greater than their own.

Many recovering people wonder if they have to believe in God to practice the Twelve Steps. The answer is *definitely not*. You don't have to be religious to practice the Twelve Steps. Agnostics, atheists, or anyone who doesn't agree with a religious-based idea of God can substitute the concept of a Higher Power. As noted earlier, your Higher Power can be defined in many ways. The Big Book tells us that the most important thing we need to know about God or a Higher Power is that we are *not* God.

ACTIVITY

IMAGINE YOUR HIGHER POWER

Do you have an image yet of your Higher Power? Write down any ideas you have so far about having a Higher Power you can trust.

_____

_____

_____

_____

_____

_____

WHAT IS SPIRITUALITY?

Spirituality is the quality of your relationship with yourself, your Higher Power, and the world. How do you know when you are growing spiritually? If you are beginning to see positive changes in your thinking, attitudes, behaviors, and relationships with others, you are growing spiritually. You are growing spiritually when you are able to let go of the belief that your ideas are almost always "right," and that you know best and others should conform to your ideas. You grow spiritually when you stop trying to control everything in your life, and you realize that there is serenity in trusting the guidance of a Higher Power.

WHY DO WE NEED SPIRITUALITY?

When you were in active addiction, you may have searched for happiness, peace, serenity, and abundance but only found a spiritual emptiness in your life. Many people who struggle with addiction try in vain to fill that void with alcohol or other drugs, money, relationships, material things, or compulsive behaviors of one type or another. But these external devices cannot resolve an internal need for spirituality. Living in recovery requires us to follow the suggestions of those with more recovery experience than we have.

Some people resist the idea of trusting a Higher Power (Step One) because they are used to being very independent and self-reliant. Remember that the Twelve Steps don't ask you to quit thinking critically. To the contrary, the Twelve Steps demand rigorous thinking, honest self-knowledge, and a deep commitment to looking beyond our own self-destructive will.

The spiritual aspect of the Twelve Step program
is a base for everything else in recovery. Spirituality helps
us let go of our self-will and self-reliance.
It's important to make spirituality the central focus of your life.

HOW CAN YOU CONNECT WITH YOUR HIGHER POWER?

If God is your Higher Power:

- **Remind yourself.** Take short breaks throughout your day to consciously remind yourself that your Higher Power is with you.

- **Show an attitude of gratitude.** Make a list of things you are thankful for, and thank your Higher Power.

- **Write to your Higher Power.** Write a letter to your Higher Power. What would you say?

- **Pray.** Ask your Higher Power to help you handle what may come each day.

If the fellowship of your Twelve Step group is your Higher Power:

- **Call and talk** with your sponsor or other people listed on your Recovery Wallet Card.

- **Find a Twelve Step meeting** to attend.

- **Keep a journal** where you write down your inner thoughts, and share them with a trusted and supportive person.

Remember that spirituality also comes in having meaningful connections with other people. Calling your sponsor is spiritual. Taking time to enjoy the peace of nature is spiritual. When spirituality is at your center, your daily actions and interactions are spiritual.

CREATE SPIRITUAL HABITS

You can grow your spirituality by adding healthy habits to your day. Check the boxes of the spiritual habits you would like to practice.

- ☐ Treat all people with the dignity and respect that belongs to all of us.

- ☐ Let go of self-pity, dishonesty, fear, control, and selfishness.

- ☐ Read the Big Book and read daily meditation books.

- ☐ Do deep-breathing exercises.

- ☐ Make time to appreciate nature.

- ☐ Practice meditation or daily prayer to calm yourself and connect with your Higher Power.

SUMMARY OF ACTIVITIES

This lesson provided an overview of the Twelve Steps. If you have time, go back and review the Twelve Steps and the twelve promises of recovery so you are familiar with them. Keep thinking about your idea of a Higher Power and how you can practice more spiritual habits in your day. Make sure you have listed some Twelve Step meetings you can attend in the Recovery Wallet Card (found in the Recovery Resources section at the end of this workbook), and keep the card with you at all times.

■ ■ ■

Duplicating this page is illegal. Do not copy this material without written permission from the publisher.

27

Step One: Understand Powerlessness

| **Thought for the Day** | *I accept that I have the disease of addiction. Now that I understand the disease, I will work hard to stay sober one day at a time.* |

POWERLESSNESS

Step One teaches us that people with the disease of addiction must come to grips with knowing that we can't control our use. We are physiologically different from other people. We can't stop using, even when faced with losing our job, our friends and family, or even our life. This is because we can't control the addicted way our mind and body react to alcohol and other drugs.

Step One:
"We admitted we were powerless over alcohol [or other drugs]—
that our lives had become unmanageable."

The words "powerless" and "unmanageable" describe a heavy reality that is hard for most of us to accept. While others can get high or drink alcohol, they can stop if they get sick or if it interferes with their family or work life.

To work on admitting powerlessness, we focus on understanding what it means to have a body and brain that can't handle drugs. When drugs hijack the reward center of the brain, it leaves us obsessed with getting and using drugs, and we are unable to stop. This is powerlessness. In other words, Step One asks us to simply admit that we need help.

To admit to being powerless over anything is a difficult and humbling experience. For many of us, admitting powerlessness is hard because it feels like giving up the hope that we can work our way out of addiction. This is why we keep fighting to control our use instead of surrendering to the idea that we have an addiction.

Duplicating this page is illegal. Do not copy this material without written permission from the publisher.

29

ACTIVITY

POWER OF ADDICTION

This activity will help you find evidence of your powerlessness against substances. In the list below, check the statements that best describe how you used alcohol or other drugs. You can also add others to the end of the list.

When I was in active addiction, I . . .

- ☐ would often drink or use when no one else was
- ☐ would drink or use at any time of the day or night
- ☐ hid the amount of alcohol or other drugs that I used
- ☐ used a drug even when I didn't know the source or quality
- ☐ brought my own booze or drugs to a party when I knew none would be there
- ☐ spent food or rent money on alcohol or other drugs
- ☐ continued to drink or use when I was already drunk or high
- ☐ lied to friends and loved ones to protect my drinking or using
- ☐ continued to use even after family and friends asked me to stop
- ☐ _____
- ☐ _____

How did your past behavior show your powerlessness over your use of alcohol and other drugs?

_____

_____

Are you ready to accept that addiction is a disease that leaves you unable to use alcohol or other drugs without losing control?

☐ Yes   ☐ No

A person with the disease of addiction is truly powerless to control his or her drug use.

LEARN ABOUT POWERLESSNESS FROM STEP ONE

Step One defines the disease of active addiction this way:

- You have a body that can't handle alcohol or other drugs.

- You have a mind that can't give them up.

- In your active addiction, you had no spiritual connection to a
Higher Power that could help you.

People who have an addiction often think they can control their use of alcohol or other drugs. Do you remember telling yourself that you could control your use by saying any of these?

- "I can quit anytime I want to."

- "If you had my life, you'd use, too."

- "I only use or drink to relax or have fun."

- "I'd know if I have a problem, and I don't."

- "If I were really addicted, I wouldn't be able to hold a job."

ACTIVITY

I CAN CONTROL IT

Take a look at the concept of control by completing the following activity, which shares Jane's story.

Jane's Story

Jane is just out of treatment. She has been sober for twenty-eight days during treatment and is feeling some sense of being able to abstain from alcohol. She feels so good, in fact, that she thinks that she may be at a point where she could actually control her drinking. Perhaps just one drink with friends wouldn't be such a big deal. After all, Jane hasn't seen these friends for almost a month.

While Jane's friends are nursing their drinks and are clearly not focused on drinking, Jane quickly downs her drink and, without thinking, orders another. Soon two turn into three, four, and five . . . and Jane winds up in bed not knowing how she got there because she blacked out.

Answer the questions on the next page.

continued

1. Why can Jane's friends control their use, but she can't? Is it because treatment was not successful? Or are there other reasons?

_____

_____

_____

_____

_____

2. If Jane truly understood that she was powerless to control her use, how would she have handled this situation differently?

_____

_____

_____

_____

_____

ADDICTION: BRAIN DISEASE OR ALLERGY?

The Big Book talks about addiction as an allergy of the body. Today we know that this "allergy," or abnormal reaction to substance use, is really a brain disease. Addiction is a physical disease of the brain.

Researchers have studied the chemistry of the addicted brain and discovered that we are not just powerless when we're using—we are powerless beforehand. Here's a great example: As soon as you think about using, your brain begins releasing dopamine, a chemical in the brain that impacts our attention, habits, mood, and feelings of pleasure. In other words, as soon as you think about taking a drink, your brain releases feel-good chemicals, and in this state, you are more likely to go ahead and take a drink or pick up another drug to intensify that good feeling.

This means that you've begun the process of relapse before the drug enters your body. Your body and brain chemistry is such that it's not possible for you to even think of alcohol or other drugs without starting the dopamine snowball effect that could lead you to drink not one, but five, ten, or twenty drinks. Your brain doesn't know the difference between actually taking a drink and simply imagining taking a drink. It reacts the same way—it wants more.

We're left with an unmanageable situation: we can't use, and we can't quit. This is where Step One begins to guide us by asking us to admit that we are powerless over the disease of addiction. We can't stop using, even when we are faced with losing everything: our job, our family, our life. Admitting powerlessness is a key step in our recovery work.

As a person with the disease of addiction, you can't control the way your mind and body react to alcohol or other drugs.
This is powerlessness.
This is why Step One is so important to your recovery.

When we understand the disease of addiction, we understand our situation, and we're no longer baffled by why we continued to use alcohol and other drugs despite the problems they caused. This understanding is the beginning of your recovery.

As you learn more about the disease of addiction, you can let go of shame and guilt. You will no longer blame yourself because you understand that no amount of willpower could have stopped your addiction. When you let go of denial, shame, and guilt, you become more comfortable with yourself and with others. This is the start of your work in recovery from the disease of addiction.

The problem that we, as people with addiction, have to come to grips with in Step One is that we can't control our use. We are physiologically different from other people. That doesn't make us bad or weak-willed—that makes us people with a disease.

Admitting powerlessness helps us:

- accept the nature of the disease of addiction
- accept that we can't control our use of substances, so we must practice complete abstinence from all mood-enhancing chemicals

POWERLESS SITUATIONS

Can you recall two situations when your drinking or other drug use was different from that of other people you were with? Think about where you were, whom you were with, and how your behavior was different from the people around you.

Situation 1

Describe where you were.

_____

_____

_____

Describe whom you were with.

_____

_____

_____

_____

How was your behavior different from others' behavior?

_____

_____

_____

_____

Situation 2

Describe where you were.

_____

_____

_____

Describe whom you were with.

_____

_____

_____

_____

How was your behavior different from others' behavior?

_____

_____

_____

_____

Compare situation 1 to situation 2

Is there a similarity in these two situations? When each of these situations was happening, what were you thinking about the people who were not drinking or using other drugs like you were?

_____

_____

_____

_____

_____

How are you different from these people?

_____

_____

_____

_____

continued

We know we've got Step One when we accept that
addiction is a disease that leaves us unable to use
substances without losing control.
We have a disease that requires complete abstinence
from alcohol and other drugs.

Even though Step One asks us to admit powerlessness, we can still feel
powerful by making positive choices. We have the power to choose to avoid risky
or "powerless" situations that could cause us to relapse. We can choose to go to
Twelve Step meetings and spend time with sober peers. We become stronger each
day by choosing not to use.

Are you ready to work Step One by admitting that you are truly powerless
to control your drinking or other drug use?

☐ Yes   ☐ No

SUMMARY OF ACTIVITIES

This lesson focused on accepting powerlessness as the foundation of Step One.
We have learned that accepting powerlessness means that people with addiction
don't have the ability to control or limit their use of alcohol or other drugs like
their nonaddicted friends. Did you explore how your drinking or other drug use
was different from other people's by completing the Powerless Situations activity?
Did you take a closer look at powerlessness by completing the I Can Control It
and Power of Addiction activities?

"Rarely have we seen a person fail who has
thoroughly followed our path."

—*Alcoholics Anonymous*

Go to Meetings

<table>
<tr><td>Thought
for the Day</td><td>"Alcoholics Anonymous [the Big Book] has all our
answers; it was written by alcoholics for alcoholics."
— THE LITTLE RED BOOK</td></tr>
</table>

THE POWER OF PEER SUPPORT

One of the most important things you can do in recovery is to engage in peer support at Twelve Step meetings. It's normal to have questions about going to meetings, and it may be hard to get yourself there—especially the first few times —but it's essential to your growth in recovery.

Twelve Step groups such as Alcoholics Anonymous (AA) or Narcotics Anonymous (NA) will not only help you maintain your sobriety but will also help you begin to develop a new way of living drug free.

EMBRACE THE BENEFITS OF MEETINGS

A Twelve Step group can help you in the following ways. Check the items that you see as the best benefits for you in attending Twelve Step meetings:

☐ You will learn about Twelve Step principles and ideas.

☐ You will receive emotional support for your recovery.

☐ It will decrease your sense of loneliness or isolation in recovery.

☐ It will give you a positive activity to do, instead of drinking or using.

☐ It will give you a new group of friends who will support your sobriety.

continued

☐ It will provide structure to help you deal with the fear and chaos of early recovery.

☐ You will demonstrate a commitment to being teachable and being willing to change.

■

HOW OFTEN SHOULD YOU ATTEND MEETINGS?

When first starting out in a Twelve Step program, it is helpful to attend meetings at least once a week. Some find it helpful to attend even more frequently. You may hear people saying that they are attending "ninety meetings in ninety days." Although this may be a positive goal for some people, it may not work for everyone. Trying to go to meetings this often can set you up for failure, and it can also interfere with all the other important recovery work you need to do. Talk with your counselor, sponsor, or friends in recovery before making a decision about the number of meetings you'll attend each week. Make sure you set a goal that's reasonable for you.

WHAT HAPPENS AT A TWELVE STEP MEETING?

Meetings range in size from six to eight people (or fewer) to several hundred people. An average-sized meeting is thirty to forty members. Most meetings last an hour or an hour and a half. People often come early or stay late to socialize with others.

The format of the meeting will vary depending on the type of meeting. A "Step meeting" will focus on a discussion of one of the Twelve Steps. A "speaker's meeting" often focuses on one person telling his or her story. Often there is time to "check in," to talk about your own experience.

There is no charge for attending Twelve Step meetings, but a small collection is usually taken to cover the cost of room rental, Twelve Step literature, etc.

Keep coming back. It works if you work it.

START ATTENDING MEETINGS

It can be hard to make yourself go to a meeting that is totally new to you. Others have felt the same way. Go to a meeting and give it a try. Experiment by going to different meetings until you find one that is a good fit for you.

When you're finding it hard to get to meetings, remember these things:

- You are not required to talk in group. It's okay just to be there for now.
- Come early and stay late. This is a good guideline for staying as long as you can at a meeting.
- Speak to at least one person at the meeting, and add these people to your Recovery Wallet Card.
- Keep it platonic. It's best not to start new romantic relationships in early recovery.
- Go to the meeting with someone else in recovery. If this will be your first meeting, it might be easier if you don't go alone.
- Keep coming back. Once you go to your first meeting, this slogan can help you keep going.

ACTIVITY

LOCATE A MEETING

To find a meeting in your area, visit the websites of Twelve Step groups, such as AA or NA. You may also want to consider attending Al-Anon meetings if you are living with someone who is still in an active addiction.

Write down any concerns you have about going to a meeting in the next week to support your recovery.

_____

_____

_____

_____

_____

_____

SUMMARY OF ACTIVITIES

This lesson focused on how the fellowship of the Twelve Step program can improve your life. Make sure you complete the Embrace the Benefits of Meetings activity to identify what you see as the best benefits for you in attending Twelve Step meetings.

■ ■ ■

Connect with a Sponsor

| Thought for the Day | *"When the student is ready, the teacher will appear."*
—ZEN PROVERB |

TWELVE STEP PROGRAMS

Twelve Step programs, such as Alcoholics Anonymous (AA) and Narcotics Anonymous (NA), are built on the idea that recovery begins when we become willing to share our stories with another human being. In the Twelve Step program, a sponsor is a person who has made progress in the recovery program and shares his or her experience with another person who is attempting to attain or maintain sobriety through working the program.

UNDERSTAND WHY YOU NEED A SPONSOR

If you are a member of a Twelve Step organization, you need a sponsor. We don't always see our life situation as clearly as others do. Allowing someone outside yourself to share his or her experiences and knowledge helps you gain insights that you may never realize on your own.

A sponsor will be able to help you work the Twelve Steps and deal with issues in your recovery. Sponsors can help monitor your progress and keep you honest and accountable so you stay on the recovery path. When times of crisis arise, your sponsor will be there for you.

Duplicating this page is illegal. Do not copy this material without written permission from the publisher.

41

WHAT DOES A SPONSOR DO?

There are many roles a sponsor can play in guiding you through recovery. Here are some of those roles:

- A sponsor can help you work the Twelve Steps by sharing his or her experiences, guidance, and encouragement.

- A sponsor can help you understand how meetings work and can introduce you to other members.

- A sponsor will listen and help you work through the difficulties of recovery.

- A sponsor can challenge you to read the Big Book, be honest in your self-inventory, and encourage you to grow as a person.

- A sponsor can be there in times of crisis.

- A sponsor can help you learn how to build positive relationships.

- A sponsor can call you on "stinking thinking" or let you know if you are "walking the walk" of recovery.

- A sponsor can support you in resisting the urge to return to alcohol or other drug use.

WHAT DOESN'T A SPONSOR DO?

- It is not a sponsor's role or responsibility to keep you in recovery or to keep you sober.

- A sponsor is not the same as a counselor or therapist. Sponsors are not trained to counsel you in this way.

- The relationship between you and your sponsor should not become a dependent one. You need to rely on your Higher Power, the fellowship of AA, and others in your support network. Your sponsor's job is to hold you accountable in building that network of support.

- A sponsor should not take advantage of or exploit you in any way.

Having a sponsor means that you won't
have to go through recovery alone.

IDENTIFY HOW A SPONSOR CAN HELP

In your own words, describe how having a sponsor might help you with your recovery.

_____

_____

_____

_____

_____

_____

_____

_____

LEARN HOW TO CHOOSE A SPONSOR

Having the right sponsor to guide you is important. It may help to talk with others in your Twelve Step group for recommendations on people who might be a good fit as your sponsor.

When looking for a sponsor, choose someone who:

- is your same gender
- has at least one year of continuous recovery
- is available to meet in person and talk on the phone
- has his or her own sponsor
- works the Steps
- is admirable in your eyes
- emphasizes the spiritual aspect of the program

If the task of finding a sponsor seems daunting, you may want to consider trying out a new sponsor on a temporary basis at first. That way you can get to know each other better before deciding whether it is a fit for both of you.

REACH OUT FOR HELP

Once you have a sponsor, it's important to communicate often. It will take time to develop a strong relationship between you and your sponsor, and it can be easy to let excuses get in the way. Remember that when your sponsor helps you, it helps your sponsor grow as well.

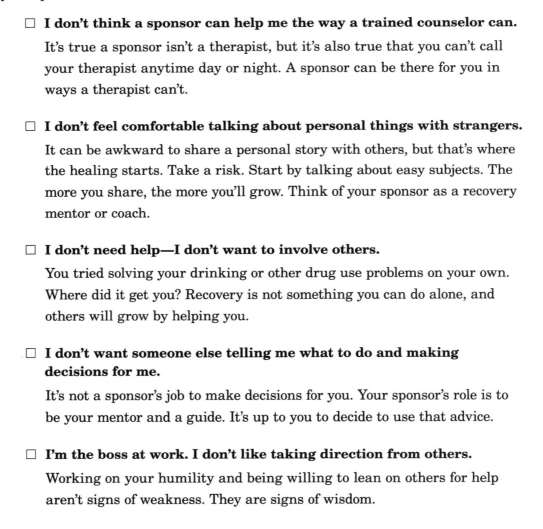

ACTIVITY

QUESTION NEGATIVE THINKING

Review the following statements. Do these thoughts sound familiar? Check the ones that you've had. These negative thoughts will keep you from talking with your sponsor.

☐ **I don't think a sponsor can help me the way a trained counselor can.**

It's true a sponsor isn't a therapist, but it's also true that you can't call your therapist anytime day or night. A sponsor can be there for you in ways a therapist can't.

☐ **I don't feel comfortable talking about personal things with strangers.**

It can be awkward to share a personal story with others, but that's where the healing starts. Take a risk. Start by talking about easy subjects. The more you share, the more you'll grow. Think of your sponsor as a recovery mentor or coach.

☐ **I don't need help—I don't want to involve others.**

You tried solving your drinking or other drug use problems on your own. Where did it get you? Recovery is not something you can do alone, and others will grow by helping you.

☐ **I don't want someone else telling me what to do and making decisions for me.**

It's not a sponsor's job to make decisions for you. Your sponsor's role is to be your mentor and a guide. It's up to you to decide to use that advice.

☐ **I'm the boss at work. I don't like taking direction from others.**

Working on your humility and being willing to lean on others for help aren't signs of weakness. They are signs of wisdom.

☐ **I don't really need to talk about all this personal stuff with someone else.**

The Twelve Steps talk about "we" and not "I." Recovery is not something that can be done alone—at least not successfully.

☐ **What if I don't like them or they don't like me?**

Start out with a temporary sponsor. That way you can see if it's a fit. But beware of leaving a sponsor because you don't like what you hear. It may be what you need.

Don't let these reasons stop you from reaching out. Having regular contact with your sponsor is essential to your success in recovery. Even if you don't feel like it, try to "fake it 'til you make it" by calling or meeting with your sponsor at least once a week until it becomes more natural.

■

SUMMARY OF ACTIVITIES

This lesson focused on helping you understand the benefits of getting a sponsor. Make sure you complete the Identify How a Sponsor Can Help and the Question Negative Thinking activities.

■ ■ ■

Create a Relapse Prevention Plan

> **Thought for the Day** | *Nothing is so bad that a drink won't make it worse.*

UNDERSTAND THE PROCESS OF RELAPSE

As noted earlier in this workbook, "relapse" can be defined as taking a drink or using after a period of abstinence. However, a relapse is really a process of losing a hold on your sobriety. It begins with warning signs that start long before a return to use occurs. If you know these warning signs, you'll be able to get help to get back on track quickly—before you use.

Research has shown that several factors contribute to a high likelihood of relapse. There are immediate factors, such as exposure to high-risk situations, a lack of coping skills, and "stinking thinking" (i.e., thinking you can control your use), that can lead to relapse. Other factors include lifestyle habits and cravings.

People in early recovery are especially susceptible to relapse. In early recovery, you are going through a lot of emotional and physical changes, and you may not yet have developed strong coping skills for dealing with life's ups and downs.

KNOW YOUR HIGH-RISK SITUATIONS

One great way to avoid a relapse is to identify and plan for high-risk situations. Certain situations or events pose a direct threat to a person's sense of control, often resulting in a relapse and return to use.

Duplicating this page is illegal. Do not copy this material without written permission from the publisher.

47

ACTIVITY

HIGH-RISK SITUATIONS

Check the items listed below that are high-risk situations for you and could cause you to relapse. As you complete this activity, think about what caused any past relapses or times when you had trouble coping with cravings.

Examples of high-risk situations include:

☐ negative emotional states, such as anger, anxiety, depression, frustration, and boredom

☐ situations that involve conflict with another person or a group of people, such as arguments with friends, coworkers, or family members

☐ events with social pressure, such as being around others who are drinking or using

☐ positive emotional events, such as celebrations

☐ exposure to alcohol or other drug-related stimuli, including seeing advertisements and driving by a bar

☐ a test of one's "willpower" by attempting a very small or limited use of substances, such as having a sip of beer

Examples of coping strategies to deal with high-risk situations include:

• Plan to call your sponsor or a friend in recovery at this time.

• Plan a fun sober activity to do during this time.

• If possible, attend a Twelve Step meeting during this period of time.

• Plan to be with other people who are supportive of your recovery during this time.

• If possible, avoid this stressful situation.

Describe the biggest high-risk situation you face and how it puts you at risk. This could be going to certain events, being around a certain person, a certain argument or conflict that keeps happening, and so on.

_____

_____

_____

_____

_____

_____

_____

_____

_____

_____

What coping strategy can you use to deal with your biggest high-risk situation?

_____

_____

_____

_____

_____

_____

Make sure you update your daily schedule to list positive activities in place of any high-risk situations you identified.

■

ENGAGE IN STRAIGHT TALK

People who relapse often focus on the immediate positive benefits of drinking alcohol or using other drugs. During times of conflict or stress, it may be easy to think of how a substance will help you deal with pain, anger, or guilt in the short term. Instead, think about how far you've come in recovery and the negative consequences you experienced while drinking or using.

If you feel tempted to use, call your sponsor immediately and talk about your feelings. Your sponsor may share a story of his or her own past relapse. Talking honestly before acting can be a huge protective factor against relapse.

Duplicating this page is illegal. Do not copy this material without written permission from the publisher.

49

ACTIVITY

CREATE A RELAPSE PREVENTION PLAN

It is very important to your recovery to create and follow a Relapse Prevention Plan. This plan will help you identify all your high-risk situations. This includes the people, places, things, events, habits, emotions, and conditions that could put your recovery at risk. Your plan will include how to cope with these situations and how to keep your life in balance.

Find the Relapse Prevention Plan in the Recovery Resources section at the end of this workbook. Fill out this plan and keep it with you as an easy reference. This Relapse Prevention Plan will help you know what people, places, and things are high risk for you—and it will contain strategies on how to avoid or deal with them.

PRACTICE RELAPSE PREVENTION

Are there times of the day that are difficult for you? Or times when you can't avoid being alone? Do you still find yourself in stressful or risky situations or feeling isolated? Keep a copy of the Relapse Prevention Strategies handout (found in the Recovery Resources section of this workbook) nearby for quick tips on handling these challenging situations, and remember to call your sponsor or other people listed on your Recovery Wallet Card for help.

KNOW HOW TO DEAL WITH A RELAPSE

Regardless of our best intentions, some people return to using alcohol or other drugs. If this happens to you, set aside any feelings of failure, immediately stop use, and get help from your sponsor or recovery support group. If you have been using for a while, you may need professional help for withdrawal. An unsupervised detoxification could be dangerous. You could experience seizures or hallucinations. Consult a reputable addiction treatment center for help. Never try to handle a relapse alone.

First Things First

If you don't stay sober, nothing else will matter.
Your first commitment must be to staying clean and sober
at least for today.

DON'T FOCUS ON FAILURES

Just because you relapse doesn't mean your recovery is a failure, and it doesn't mean you'll return to regular use or a life of chronic addiction. Focusing on the negative leads to guilt, blame, and resentment toward yourself—sure ways to sabotage any positive progress you've made in recovery. Instead, look at it as a temporary setback. If you make a mistake, reach out for help from the people you listed on your Recovery Wallet Card, such as your sponsor, Twelve Step peers, or your counselor. Also refer to the End Your Lapse tips on the Recovery Wallet Card.

SUMMARY OF ACTIVITIES

This lesson focused on relapse prevention and asked you to create a Relapse Prevention Plan that is specific to your situation and challenges. Make sure you reference the Relapse Prevention Strategies handout (found in the Recovery Resources section at the end of this workbook) for quick tips on handling challenging situations. Also make sure you have your Recovery Wallet Card with you at all times so you can easily identify the people you can count on for support.

■ ■ ■

Duplicating this page is illegal. Do not copy this material without written permission from the publisher.

51

Recovery Resources

Workbook 1

Trash Your Stash Checklist

Clearing your living environment of anything that reminds you of drug use is the first step in protecting your abstinence. Don't do this alone! Ask your sponsor or a friend in recovery to make sure you completely trash your stash—including related things such as smoking pipes, bongs, or needles. Use the checklist below to help you get rid of anything that will trigger memories of drinking and/or using.

ADD TO YOUR ENVIRONMENT	REMOVE FROM YOUR ENVIRONMENT
☐ Place Twelve Step literature, the Serenity Prayer, favorite recovery slogans, and the Big Book in the places you used to have your stash.	☐ Remove all alcohol, other drugs, and paraphernalia from your environment.
☐ Add contact information for your sponsor, your counselor, and friends from Twelve Step meetings to your cell phone.	☐ Delete your drug dealers' and/or drinking buddies' phone numbers from your address book. Remove any notes or pieces of paper with names and numbers of dealers and/or drinking buddies.
☐ Bookmark positive websites on your computer (such as Alcoholics Anonymous and Narcotics Anonymous).	☐ Remove the email addresses of drug dealers and/or drinking buddies.
☐ Save music and movies that will provide uplifting messages to support your sobriety.	☐ Remove bookmarks from websites that trigger your desire to drink or use drugs.
☐ Use medications that have been prescribed to you only as directed. Mark medications on your calendar or smartphone to remind you to take them on time.	☐ Get rid of music, concert T-shirts, hats, and other things that trigger your desire to drink or use drugs.
☐ Attach a schedule of local Twelve Step meetings to your refrigerator.	☐ Get rid of movies with drinking or drug themes.
	☐ Get rid of any addictive medications.

Medication Guide for People in Recovery

Many medications, both over-the-counter (OTC) and prescription (Rx), have mood-altering effects. Not only do these medications have addiction potential of their own, but they may also lead to relapse.

This guide lists some common medications to avoid and others that are safer to use. However, it is not meant to replace the advice of a physician, pharmacist, or other health care professional. If you have any questions regarding medication use during your recovery, please contact your physician and/or pharmacist.

Moreover, this guide is not exhaustive. With so many medications on the market, it is impossible to list them all. Instead, you'll simply find a few common examples in various medication categories. Again, if you have questions about a specific medication not listed in this guide, contact your physician and your recovery team (counselor or peer coach).

Most medications are listed here by generic name—that is, by their active ingredient—with an example of the brand name in parentheses: for example, acetaminophen (Tylenol). Some medications are sold under many brand names. Check the label for the active ingredients; any brand-name medication package should also include its generic name.

Symbols used in this guide:

Rx = prescription only

OTC = over-the-counter

General Guidelines

Be up-front with your physician and/or pharmacist about your addiction. If they are aware of it, they can prescribe or recommend more suitable medications.

Important: read all labels. Many OTC medications contain one or more ingredients that you should not be taking. Check both the active and inactive ingredients, as many contain alcohol as an "inactive" ingredient. If a medication that you should not be taking is deemed medically necessary by your health care professional, notify your sponsor as well as your recovery team. Make a plan for use as well as a plan to discontinue use.

Cold, Allergy, and Asthma Medications

Avoid the ingredient pseudoephedrine, which has stimulant-like properties and is contained in most OTC cold and sinus preparations.

Avoid these and other pseudoephedrine-containing OTC medications:

- Sudafed
- Tylenol Cold & Sinus
- DayQuil
- Alavert D-12
- Advil Cold & Sinus
- Claritin-D
- Theraflu
- Mucinex D
- Zyrtec-D

Other cold/allergy/asthma OTC medications to avoid:

- diphenhydramine (Benadryl)
- chlorpheniramine (Chlor-Trimeton)
- clemastine (Tavist)
- brompheniramine (Dimetapp Elixir)
- ephedrine (Bronkaid, Primatene)
- dextromethorphan (Robitussin DM, or any cough syrup with "DM")
- nighttime preparations, since most contain alcohol (e.g., NyQuil)

Safe medications for cold, sinus, and allergy symptoms:

- loratadine (Claritin, Alavert). **Beware:** Claritin-D and Alavert D-12 contain pseudoephedrine. Make sure you are using the pseudoephedrine-free medication.
- saline nasal spray (Ocean)
- Vicks VapoRub, Vicks steam
- guaifenesin (Mucinex, Vicks 44E)
- benzonatate (Tessalon Perles—Rx)
- NasalCrom nasal spray
- cough drops (such as Halls)
- sore throat lozenges
- salt-water gargle
- Breathe Right nasal strips

Pain Medications

The first thing you need to say at any visit to an emergency room or to a physician prescribing you pain medication is that you are recovering from an addiction. The physician and you will then create a plan to resolve your pain and maintain your sobriety.

Avoid all opioids:

Opioids are the most powerful known pain relievers. Naturally occurring opium derivatives include morphine and codeine. Partially synthetic derivatives of morphine include heroin, oxycodone, and oxymorphone. Synthetic opioid compounds include fentanyl, alfentanil, levorphanol, meperidine, methadone, and propoxyphene.

Avoid these and other opioid Rx pain medications:

- fentanyl (Duragesic patch)
- morphine (Avinza and other brands)
- codeine (Tylenol #3)
- oxycodone (Percodan, Percocet, OxyContin)
- hydrocodone (Vicodin, Vicoprofen, Lortab)
- hydromorphone (Dilaudid)
- propoxyphene (Darvon, Darvocet)
- oxymorphone (Opana)
- tramadol (Ultram, Ultracet)

For pain relief, some physicians prescribe other medications, such as antidepressants, that are also mood altering and addictive. Check this guide or talk to your doctor before adding them to your treatment plan. Avoid using all benzodiazepines (listed under "Psychiatric Medications" on the next page).

Be careful with dental procedures. Tell your dentist you'd like to avoid nitrous oxide or "laughing gas." Injectable medications such as lidocaine or Novocaine are better because they provide the numbing pain relief without the mind-altering effect.

Safe pain medications:

Unless your doctor has told you to avoid these medications, they are generally safe (not addictive or mood altering) to use for pain:

- aspirin (Bayer)—OTC
- ibuprofen (Motrin, Advil)—OTC
- acetaminophen (Tylenol)—OTC
- naproxen (Naprosyn, Aleve)—OTC
- celecoxib (Celebrex)—Rx
- ketorolac (Toradol)—Rx
- methotrexate (Rheumatrex)—Rx
- infliximab (Remicade)—Rx
- and many more

Psychiatric Medications

Most medications that are used for anxiety, depression, and other neurological disorders are mood altering. Some of these are safe and nonaddictive, and some are not. If you are diagnosed with a neurological disorder, work with your doctor to pick the safest one that will handle your symptoms. If you are already on a medication, talk to your doctor before discontinuing its use. Some of these medications have severe withdrawal effects that require tapering down the dose.

Avoid all benzodiazepines:

- diazepam (Valium)
- oxazepam (Serax)
- alprazolam (Xanax)
- midazolam (Versed)
- lorazepam (Ativan)
- clonazepam (Klonopin)

Some acceptable Rx psychiatric medications:

- fluoxetine (Prozac)
- sertraline (Zoloft)
- paroxetine (Paxil)
- citalopram (Celexa)
- escitalopram (Lexapro)
- bupropion (Wellbutrin)
- venlafaxine (Effexor)
- amitriptyline (Elavil)
- imipramine (Tofranil)
- nortriptyline (Aventyl, Pamelor)
- clomipramine (Anafranil)
- buspirone (BuSpar)

Some anticonvulsant and antipsychotic Rx medications to avoid:

- clozapine (Clozaril)
- olanzapine (Zyprexa)
- phenytoin (Dilantin)
- risperidone (Risperdal)
- phenobarbital (Luminal)

Most medications used for attention-deficit/hyperactivity disorder (ADHD/ADD) have a stimulant property. You should try to avoid:

- methylphenidate (Ritalin)—Rx
- dextroamphetamine (Adderall)—Rx
- lisdexamfetamine (Vyvanse)—Rx

A safe medication for ADHD is:

- atomoxetine (Strattera)—Rx

Common Medications

Diet medications:

The majority of diet medications have stimulant properties; many contain actual amphetamines, which are extremely addictive. *Therefore, it is highly recommended that you avoid all of these types of medications.*

Some specific examples of diet pills that should be *avoided* are:

- sibutramine (Meridia)—Rx
- phentermine (Adipex)—Rx
- dextroamphetamine (Dexedrine)—Rx

Acceptable heartburn/upset stomach medications:

- omeprazole (Prilosec)
- ranitidine (Zantac)
- antacids such as Tums, Maalox, Mylanta, Rolaids; famotidine (Pepcid)

Acceptable diarrhea medications:

- loperamide (Imodium A-D)
- bismuth subsalicylate (Kaopectate)

Acceptable constipation medications:

These medications should all be avoided if you have an eating disorder. If you do not, the following medications can be taken:

- docusate sodium (Colace)
- senna (Senokot)
- Metamucil powder

Mouthwash:

Many OTC mouthwashes contain from 9 to 21 percent alcohol.

Avoid any alcohol-containing brands, such as:

- Listerine
- Cepacol
- Plax
- Scope

Some mouthwash brands that are okay to use:

- Colgate
- Act
- FluoriGard
- Act Kids

Sleep agents:

It is best to avoid all sleep medications since they have depressant-like properties. The best treatment for insomnia is to find ways to relax: meditate, listen to music, or take a hot bath before bed. Try to find something that works for you. If you still have difficulty falling or staying asleep, discuss this with your physician and recovery team.

Sleep medications to avoid:

- doxylamine (Unisom)—OTC
- diphenhydramine (Sominex)—OTC
- zolpidem (Ambien)—Rx
- zaleplon (Sonata)—Rx

Motion sickness agents:

Most of these cause mood-altering effects and should be avoided. A few examples of motion sickness medications to avoid:

- meclizine (Bonine)—OTC; Antivert—Rx
- dimenhydrinate (Dramamine)—OTC
- scopolamine patch (Transderm Scop)—Rx

Daily Schedule

Photocopy this form, so you have one for each day of the week. Then fill in each hour of the schedule.

Daily Schedule

Day of the Week (circle one):   M   T   W   Th   F   Sat   Sun

A.M.   6:00: _____

7:00: _____

8:00: _____

9:00: _____

10:00: _____

11:00: _____

P.M.   Noon: _____

1:00: _____

2:00: _____

3:00: _____

4:00: _____

5:00: _____

6:00: _____

7:00: _____

8:00: _____

9:00: _____

10:00: _____

11:00: _____

Notes:

Reminders

Ask yourself these questions:
- Have I filled in gaps of time?
- Have I scheduled time to connect with my sponsor and Higher Power?
- Have I identified and planned for high-risk situations?
- Did I make my recovery activities a priority?
- Is my day too busy or too stressful?
- Did I schedule time to attend at least one Twelve Step meeting per week?
- Have I shared my plan with others?

Keep this schedule with you at all times.
If you use a smartphone or computer calendar, input the schedule
into that system so you see it every day.

Recovery Wallet Card

Step 1: Write down the names and contact information for three people you know you can count on to support your recovery.

Step 2: Write down three reasons why you want to stay sober. Make sure your reasons are about gaining something positive for yourself and not about avoiding something negative.

Step 3: Write down the names, addresses, and meeting times for nearby Twelve Step meetings you can attend. You can include other recovery resources, such as the addresses and times for addiction treatment meetings or meetings with a mental health counselor or other provider.

Step 4: Keep a copy of the Recovery Wallet Card with you at all times. It's also a good idea to input your supporters into your phone contacts.

Recovery Wallet Card Example

My supporters:	My reasons for being in recovery:
Name: Wesley A. **Phone:** 612-495-XXXX **Name:** Jennifer A. **Phone:** 651-375-XXXX **Name:** Mike R. (my sponsor) **Phone:** 651-984-XXXX	1. Become someone whom I and others respect. 2. Heal with my mom/love my mom. 3. Be good to myself and others. Happy life. *"One day at a time"*
My recovery resources/meetings: **Name:** Sober Friends (Cafe Coffee Shop) **Address:** 9459 W. 28th St., Minneapolis, MN 55408 **Day/Time:** M-F, 7 a.m. **Name:** Big Book Study Group **Address:** 4241 Lyndale Ave., Minneapolis, MN 55408 **Day/Time:** Wed., 6 p.m. **Name:** Solution Seekers (Santi Community Center) **Address:** 1945 Hawkens St. NW, Eagan, MN 55122 **Day/Time:** Sat., 6 p.m.	**END YOUR LAPSE** 1. ASK FOR HELP TO STOP USING 2. GET OUT OF THE SITUATION 3. REPEAT THE FOLLOWING • *I made a mistake.* • *I feel guilty, but that's normal.* • *I will stay calm.* • *One slip does not equal failure.* • *I can learn from this experience.* • *I can recommit to my recovery.*

Your Recovery Wallet Card

Fill out your information.

cut on solid line

My supporters:

Name: _____

Phone: _____

Name: _____

Phone: _____

Name: _____

Phone: _____

My reasons for being in recovery:

1. _____

2. _____

3. _____

"One day at a time"

← fold in half
on dotted line

My recovery resources/meetings:

Name: _____

Address: _____

Day/Time: _____

Name: _____

Address: _____

Day/Time: _____

Name: _____

Address: _____

Day/Time: _____

END YOUR LAPSE

1. ASK FOR HELP TO STOP USING
2. GET OUT OF THE SITUATION
3. REPEAT THE FOLLOWING
   - *I made a mistake.*
   - *I feel guilty, but that's normal.*
   - *I will stay calm.*
   - *One slip does not equal failure.*
   - *I can learn from this experience.*
   - *I can recommit to my recovery.*

← fold in half
on dotted line

PAGE 2 OF 2

Twelve Steps

Where Did the Twelve Steps Come From?

Until 1934, there was no known addiction treatment that worked. Later that year, Bill W. and Dr. Bob started a group called Alcoholics Anonymous (AA) and eventually wrote the Twelve Steps to offer simple, straightforward principles, or basic truths, that people can follow to recover from addiction. The Twelve Steps express the fundamental principles used by members of AA to transform their lives from moral decay and early death to a spiritual fitness needed to keep the disease of addiction at bay.

THE TWELVE STEPS OF ALCOHOLICS ANONYMOUS

1. We admitted we were powerless over alcohol [or other drugs]—that our lives had become unmanageable.

2. Came to believe that a Power greater than ourselves could restore us to sanity.

3. Made a decision to turn our will and our lives over to the care of God *as we understood Him.*

4. Made a searching and fearless moral inventory of ourselves.

5. Admitted to God, to ourselves, and to another human being the exact nature of our wrongs.

6. Were entirely ready to have God remove all these defects of character.

7. Humbly asked Him to remove our shortcomings.

8. Made a list of all persons we had harmed, and became willing to make amends to them all.

9. Made direct amends to such people wherever possible, except when to do so would injure them or others.

10. Continued to take personal inventory and when we were wrong promptly admitted it.

11. Sought through prayer and meditation to improve our conscious contact with God *as we understood Him,* praying only for knowledge of His will for us and the power to carry that out.

12. Having had a spiritual awakening as the result of these steps, we tried to carry this message to alcoholics, and to practice these principles in all our affairs.*

* Reprinted from *Alcoholics Anonymous,* 4th ed. (New York: Alcoholics Anonymous World Services, Inc., 2001), 59–60.

Relapse Prevention Plan

PART 1

This activity will help you create your own personalized relapse prevention plan. This is a three-part activity. Be sure to complete all three parts. Also, periodically update your relapse prevention plan as your routines and environment change.

It is important to identify your high-risk situations or events when you used to drink or use other drugs. These situations or events can be stressful and pose a direct threat to your recovery. It pays to be prepared and plan out the coping strategies you will use.

1. Name four PEOPLE (by first name only to preserve confidentiality) you used with before treatment who are still using and whom you might or will meet again.

   1. _____
   2. _____
   3. _____
   4. _____

2. Write down the names of four PLACES where you used in the past that might still be tempting for you.

   1. _____
   2. _____
   3. _____
   4. _____

3. Name four THINGS that you used to get high (e.g., needles, pipes, money, razors, mirrors, or pills) that might trigger a craving.

   1. _____
   2. _____
   3. _____
   4. _____

4. Describe four HABITS that you had and might still associate with using (e.g., taking a certain route to work, driving by a dealer's house, going to a liquor store, or seeing commercials, logos, or clothing).

    1. _____
    2. _____
    3. _____
    4. _____

5. List four EMOTIONS that could cause a craving (e.g., angry, sad, scared, excited, or bored).

    1. _____
    2. _____
    3. _____
    4. _____

6. List four CONDITIONS that might start a craving (e.g., being out of touch with support people, HALT [hungry, angry, lonely, tired], medical problems, or poverty).

    1. _____
    2. _____
    3. _____
    4. _____

7. Review the high-risk situations/triggers that you listed above. Write down the four most important HIGH-RISK SITUATIONS from these lists.

    1. _____
    2. _____
    3. _____
    4. _____

Relapse Prevention Plan

PART 2

Now that you have made the decision to quit drinking and using drugs, you will begin to feel more confident about staying sober, and this confidence will grow as you continue your recovery journey. However, you still need to plan for risky situations that pose a threat to your recovery. This relapse prevention plan will help you watch for relapse warning signs.

1. List three negative emotional states (e.g., anger, anxiety, depression, frustration, boredom, or grief).

   1. _____
   2. _____
   3. _____

2. What do you intend to do when you find yourself feeling these emotional states?

   1. _____
   2. _____
   3. _____

3. Situations that cause you to experience challenging emotional states and conflict in relationships will put you at a high risk of relapse. List three possible situations and people who might produce challenging emotions or conflict in your life.

   Situations

   1. _____
   2. _____
   3. _____

   People

   1. _____
   2. _____
   3. _____

4. What do you intend to do when you find yourself in these negative
   emotional states?

   1. _____

   2. _____

   3. _____

5. Describe three examples of social pressure (including verbal or nonverbal
   persuasion or indirect pressure) that might lead you to return to substance use.

   1. _____

   2. _____

   3. _____

6. What do you intend to do when you find yourself in situations where you
   feel social pressure?

   1. _____

   2. _____

   3. _____

7. List three positive emotional states that you think could be a problem for you
   (e.g., happiness, excitement, feeling comfortable, or wanting to celebrate).

   1. _____

   2. _____

   3. _____

8. What do you intend to do when you find yourself feeling these positive
   emotional states?

   1. _____

   2. _____

   3. _____

9. Give three examples of times when you rationalized your use (e.g., buying a bottle of liquor in case a guest drops in). Denial and a desire for immediate gratification will increase your vulnerability to return to substance use.

   1. _____
   2. _____
   3. _____

10. What do you intend to do when you find yourself rationalizing or denying these situations?

   1. _____
   2. _____
   3. _____

11. A balanced lifestyle has been found to be the strongest defense against relapse. What areas of your life are out of balance?

   1. _____
   2. _____
   3. _____

12. What do you intend to do when you find your life out of balance?

   1. _____
   2. _____
   3. _____

13. What have you been doing (or not doing) for your physical well-being lately?

   _____
   _____
   _____
   _____
   _____

14. What have you been doing (or not doing) for your mental well-being lately?

_____

_____

_____

_____

_____

15. What have you been doing (or not doing) for your spiritual well-being lately?

_____

_____

_____

_____

_____

Keep in Mind: Structure and overall balance are critical for staying in recovery. And remember, if you need support, you can call one of your contacts from your Recovery Wallet Card, including your sponsor, counselor, supportive family members, or friends from meetings.

Relapse Prevention Plan

PART 3

Finding Support: It is important to know where you can find help when you need it.

1. List five people (by first name only) you can call for help when you need it.

    1. _____

    2. _____

    3. _____

    4. _____

    5. _____

2. List five places (addresses and phone numbers) where you can go for help when you need it.

    1. _____

    2. _____

    3. _____

    4. _____

    5. _____

3. List five thoughts that will motivate you to prevent a relapse.

    1. _____

    2. _____

    3. _____

    4. _____

    5. _____

4. If you are unable to follow the strategies in this relapse prevention plan, what can you do?

_____

_____

_____

_____

_____

Remember that your counselor and sponsor are there for you. All you need to do is reach out.

Relapse Prevention Strategies

1. Are there certain times of day that are very stressful for you? Are there days or times (such as payday or the weekend) when you previously used drugs?

   Strategies:
   - Plan to call your sponsor or a friend in recovery at this time.
   - Plan a fun sober activity to do during this time.
   - If possible, attend a Twelve Step meeting during this period of time.
   - Plan to be with other people who are supportive of your recovery during this time.
   - Plan to work on your program during this time—read the Big Book, Twelve Step literature, or a meditation book; spend time in meditation.

2. Are there stretches of time when you will be alone?

   Strategies:
   - Try to limit the long periods of time that you are spending alone.
   - Plan to call your sponsor or a friend in recovery at this time.
   - Plan a fun sober activity to do during this time.
   - If possible, attend a Twelve Step meeting during this time.
   - Plan to be with other people who are supportive of your recovery during this time.

3. Are there events that will be stressful for you?

   Strategies:
   - If possible, avoid this stressful situation.
   - Limit the number of stressful situations you have in your day. Can you say no to something?
   - Before you go to this stressful event, call your sponsor or a friend in recovery. Talk through strategies to handle the stress.
   - Have a plan of "escape" if the situation becomes too stressful—drive separately to the event, for example.
   - Make a plan to call your sponsor or a friend in recovery right after the stressful event.
   - Go to a Twelve Step meeting right after the stressful event.

- Plan an enjoyable sober activity to do right after the stressful event.
- Spend some time in meditation before and after the event.
- Use breathing exercises to calm yourself during the event.

4. Are there any high-risk situations for you this week (people and places you should avoid)? Avoid these high-risk situations—the places where you used to use and places where other people will be using.

Tips for avoiding places:

- Take a different route so you avoid certain places.
- Ask people to meet you at locations that will not trigger use for you— for example, meet at a coffee shop rather than a bar.
- Ask other people to drive, so you aren't tempted to go places you shouldn't.
- Turn down invitations to events where alcohol or other drugs might be present.

Tips for avoiding people:

- Politely say no to people you need to avoid.
- Honestly tell people that you are in recovery now and need to protect your sobriety.
- Get rid of the phone numbers and email addresses of people you used to use with.
- Don't go to places where you know these people will be.
- Avoid all contact, even by phone, with these people.

If you can't avoid a situation, use these coping strategies:

- Ask someone who is supportive of your recovery to go with you.
- Talk through the situation with your sponsor or a friend in recovery before going.
- Write out a plan of how you are going to handle the situation. Create this plan with the help of a friend in recovery. Carry this plan with you.
- Commit to call your sponsor or a friend in recovery right after the event or situation.
- Have an "escape" plan to get out of the situation if it becomes too difficult for you.
- Plan to go to a Twelve Step event right afterward.

About Hazelden Publishing

As part of the Hazelden Betty Ford Foundation, Hazelden Publishing offers both cutting-edge educational resources and inspirational books. Our print and digital works help guide individuals in treatment and recovery, and their loved ones. Professionals who work to prevent and treat addiction also turn to Hazelden Publishing for evidence-based curricula, digital content solutions, and videos for use in schools, treatment programs, correctional programs, and electronic health records systems. We also offer training for implementation of our curricula.

Through published and digital works, Hazelden Publishing extends the reach of healing and hope to individuals, families, and communities affected by addiction and related issues.

For more information about Hazelden publications,
please call **800-328-9000**
or visit us online at **hazelden.org/bookstore**.